LIFE
OR DEATH
בחיים

MOSAICA PRESS

LIFE OR DEATH
שאול ובחיים

FACING END-OF-LIFE ISSUES IN THE MODERN WORLD

—

Rabbi Tanchum S. Burton,
LSW, CDLTEA, MH

Mosaica Press, Inc.
© 2018 by Mosaica Press
Designed by Rayzel Broyde
Typeset by Brocha Mirel Strizower

ISBN-10: 1-946351-39-3
ISBN-13: 978-1-946351-39-5

Published by:
Mosaica Press, Inc.
www.mosaicapress.com
info@mosaicapress.com

RABBI YAAKOV HILLEL
ROSH YESHIVAT
HEVRAT AHAVAT SHALOM
45 ARZEY HABIRA ST. JERUSALEM

יעקב משה הלל
ראש ישיבת
חברת אהבת שלום
רח׳ ארזי הבירה 45 ירושלים

2nd of Sh'vat, 5778

A Letter of Approbation

I have carefully read the treatise called **"Life or Death"** published by my dear friend, Rabbi **Avraham Shmuel Gross** shlit"a. The pamphlet is aimed at explaining to the general public what horrendous things are being done to hasten the deaths of mortally ill patients and those on their deathbed. These practices are done for various reasons: to save the money and effort necessary to keep them alive, or out of concern that terrible suffering and physical malfunctioning make their lives unbearable, or to remove organs from them that could save the lives of other patients. Therefore, these people's lives are terminated, either with their consent, or their family's consent, or without any consent. They are killed through various "merciful" methods, such as detaching them from respirators, starvation, and poisoning, all as euthanasia to lighten the suffering of the patients and their families.

The greatest rabbis of our generations established clearly that all of these methods of killing patients are forbidden; they are considered murder, or indirect manslaughter, and are not permitted at all.

Since most people are not aware of their legal rights to request and stipulate how they should be treated in accordance with the demands of *halachah*, or how their family can request so on their behalf, to prevent any harm at all to the patient's life, this treatise explains in a clear fashion, in English, the opinion and viewpoint of the rabbinical leaders on this subject regarding determining the time of death according to the *halachah*, and how to guard the patient's life so that he not be harmed in any way, and to recommend at every stage and situation that involves doubt about what to do and how to do it, that the doctors should consult with a rabbi who is well versed on this topic, and follow his directives.

Aside from the *halachic* directives presented in this treatise concerning this serious subject, the basic civil laws that apply to all of these situations are explained in short, in order to stimulate the patient and his family to contact professionals in their city who can provide expert advice and help concerning the practical issues involved in saving lives.

My above-mentioned friend thus merited to greatly benefit both the deceased and the living, which is really true lovingkindness. There is no doubt that when this treatise will spread throughout the world, many will follow its directives, and great numbers of people will be delivered from death and murder. If our sages said (*Mishnah Sanhedrin* 4:5) that every person who saves a Jewish life is as though he upheld an entire world, my friend's merit is tremendous, for he will save many from death, and merit to uphold many worlds; he should be praised for his worthy deed.

I hereby bless him and his entire family with blessings for success, both spiritual and material. May all of his endeavors be blessed, Amen.

Rabbi I. Scheiner
Dean of Kamenitzer Yeshiva
51 Zephania St., Jerusalem
Tel. (972-2) 532-2512; 532-3664
Cell. (972)533-196-968
〜

הרב יצחק שיינר
ראש ישיבת קמניץ
רחוב צפני' 51, ירושלים
02-532-3664 ;02-532-2512 טל.
0533-196-968
〜

בס"ד

ישלח דברו

To the honored Oskim "ע',
re prolongation of life,

I saw the wonderful
Kuntres you published,
and it won much praise
in my heart. All that
is written there is true
according to the Torah,
and I pray that you succeed
in your important task.

יצחק שיינר

הן אמנם פשוט וברור דאף על גב שהחיים של משותקים ל"ע אינם כלל חיים לפי המושגים הפשוטים שלנו וקשה מאד כח הסבל של החולה וגם של משפחתו, עם כל זאת הננו מצווים וגם חייבים להשתדל בקום ועשה להארכת חייהם של משותקים, ואם הוא חולה חייבים ודאי להזדרז בהצלתו וגם לחלל עליו את השבת, כי הענין של "חיים" אין לנו שום קנה-מידה כמה למדוד את יוקרם וחשיבותם אפילו לא בתורה ומצוות, שהרי מחללין את השבת גם על זקן חולה מוכה שחין אף על פי שהוא חרש ושוטה גמור, ואינו יכול לעשות שום מצוה וחייו הם רק למשא וסבל גדול על משפחתו וגורם להם ביטול תורה ומצוות, ונוסף לצערם הגדול הרי הם אזלי ומדלדלי, אפילו הכי מצוה בגדולי ישראל להשתדל להצלתו ולעסוק בהצלתו ולחלל עליו את השבת.

הרה"ג רבי שלמה זלמן אויערבאך זללה"ה
מספרו מנחת שלמה ח"א סימן צא ס"ק כד

Table of Contents

Preface

Who Should Read This Booklet

Illness and death affect all human beings, and the decisions regarding a person struggling with disease or nearing the end of his life will be decisions that each and every one of us will likely have to make at some point. This publication has been created to educate people about how Judaism relates to this difficult but very meaningful challenge. It is intended to serve as a set of answers to questions that naturally arise for people who, when faced with their own health crises or that of their loved ones, need to get their bearings.

Critical medical situations are overwhelming in and of themselves, but there are phenomena occurring in the world that complicate these issues further. The growing trend in many contemporary societies toward euthanasia and physician-assisted suicide poses a threat to the values of Jews worldwide, both from a religious and a human standpoint. When it comes to our responsibility toward a severely ill or dying patient, the Torah is very clear that *pikuach nefesh*, saving and prolonging life, is the guiding principle. But today, societal institutions that are supposed to be dedicated to health and healing are becoming contaminated with notions of "assisted dying." It is therefore equally urgent for us to be reminded of an even higher and more all-encompassing Jewish precept: the sanctity of life itself.

Therefore, whether the patient is you, your family members, loved ones, community peers, or your congregants, the information contained within these pages is intended for you. But do not think that this booklet was compiled for informational purposes alone. Besides equipping the reader with sources and parameters within which to understand these issues, the purpose of this booklet is to raise consciousness among Jewish people everywhere.

Each one of us must know clearly that euthanasia and physician-assisted suicide are completely against what we believe; that no matter how "legitimate" these practices become in contemporary life, we must insist on our own values of *pikuach nefesh*; that no matter how forcefully medical professionals push these agendas, we must be educated and insist on handling our issues in the light of Torah, even if that means that we have to fight tooth and nail.

The Doctor's Prognosis Is Not the Final Word

Mrs. M. was a very active artist, grandmother, cook, and tennis player, well into her eighties, when she was afflicted with cancer. The hospital in downtown Toronto told her there was nothing more they could do for her and they wished to withdraw her feeding and hydration tubes.

The family was told that she would not live through the weekend. I went to say goodbye on a Thursday night. During the visit, the doctor, a young Jewish palliative care specialist, came by to tell the family that he thought they should take the necessary steps to end her life. They told that to Mrs. M. as well.

After the doctor left her room, we had a warm, wonderful, deep conversation and we laughed wholeheartedly. When I left the room, I had a strange feeling that I would see her again and my final words were, "Goodbye Mrs. M., I'll see you again real soon."

The family decided to fight against the doctor's wishes and did not agree to withhold the feeding tubes. As such, Mrs. M. lived through the weekend, and on Monday the hospital told her they would have to transfer her to another hospital, as their hospital did not have a palliative care wing. She was transferred to the hospital where I volunteer.

When she entered, the oncologist felt that Mrs. M. had but a few minutes left to live. But instead of doing nothing, she decided to try a new drug. Fortunately, and to everyone's surprise, the drug had an extremely positive effect. About two weeks later, Mrs. M. went home. She began to regain her strength and took up art and even tennis once again.

Over the next year, she would witness the marriage of two grandchildren and the birth of three new great-grandchildren. After that time, her cancer returned and she eventually succumbed to the illness. But not before experiencing perhaps the best year of her life, surrounded by family and dear friends.

(Heard from Rabbi Zale Newman)

WHEN BIKUR CHOLIM BECOMES PIKUACH NEFESH

To be involved in the holy work of *bikur cholim* is to perform one of the greatest acts of kindness: easing the burden of a fellow Jew who has become ill. Visiting the sick allows us to emulate G-d. It is a practice we learn from Hashem Himself, Who visited Avraham Avinu while he was recovering from the "surgery" of *bris milah*. To be there for someone in recovery—to understand their pain, to listen to their worries and concerns—is an incredible endeavor. The Gemara tells us, "These are the things that bring benefit to a person in this world while the main reward awaits him in the World to Come...*bikur cholim*."[1] Among the spiritual benefits to the person performing *bikur*

---

1   *Shabbos* 127a. In *Peah* 1:1, the Mishnah also counts *bikur cholim* among the positive mitzvos in the category of *gemilas chassadim*, as having no upper limit to which a person should be physically involved. With regard to the amount of money or assets a person should spend on a positive mitzvah, however, the upper limit is twenty percent of their total assets, because more than that places him or her at risk. When it comes to a negative mitzvah, or *lo sa'aseh*, on the other hand, a person is required to give everything he or she owns not to transgress; risk is not a factor (see Rabbi Akiva Eiger, loc. cit.). That's why, when a *bikur cholim* worker is in the position to defend the life of a patient, the worker has to do everything possible.

cholim is the opportunity to think and see beyond his own needs, to become a person concerned with alleviating others' pain, and to achieve majesty as a compassionate human being.

One does not need an official title or role to be a visitor of the sick, or *mevaker cholim*. And the fact is that nearly everyone will find himself in this role at some point or another. We are all ready to do this for our loved ones, our friends, and the members of our community. It is an integral part of family life, an inescapable part of the life cycle. We can breathe a sigh of relief, knowing that the Torah gives us a precise outline regarding what to do in this situation, should we arrive there. For this reason, the contents of this booklet are addressed to everyone: rabbi, volunteer, friend, parent, child, and sibling.

If all we needed to be concerned about was what to do for another person who has taken ill or is at the end of his life, a simple manual on how to perform *bikur cholim* would be sufficient. This booklet does not address itself to the importance of visiting the sick, but rather the very real possibility that anyone living in a contemporary Western society may at some point have to act to save the life of an ill person. He may have to save another's life from secular values that do not affirm life, and potentially, from doctors who espouse these life-negating values.

HEALING

There are many involved in the healing process of a person. First and foremost, of course, is Hashem, as the verse states,

"I am G-d, your Healer."[2] But on Earth, there is a whole team of people—from the primary care physician to the admissions secretary, from the interns and volunteers to the nurses, surgeons, and specialists—who contribute something to a patient's well-being. As emissaries from Heaven, all of these people work together to bring healing to the sick. And you too, no matter what your exact relationship is to the patient, are part of this team. Your listening to the needs of the patient, communicating them to the staff, advocating for the patient when they can't do that for themselves, and being there when everyone else is busy at work facilitates the healing process.

At the same time, your mission is very different from that of the other members of this team. Your responsibility toward a hospital patient comes from your accountability to Hashem and His Torah. You might be the only member of this team who is concerned with what the Torah demands of people involved in healthcare. Unless you are working in a medical setting governed by the values of Torah and halachah, you may be alone in your awareness of these things. In general, your Torah values will not place you in conflict with your working environment. As long as you and the medical professionals around you share the goal of promoting and protecting the health of the patient, you can and must work together with them as a team.

There are certain situations, however, where promoting and protecting the health of a patient is no longer the medical staff's goal. Perhaps the patient's disease has worsened to the point where the doctors decide that his illness is incurable.

Perhaps the patient's condition has become so painful that her family members consider her life not worth living. Perhaps the patient himself, because of his illness, has lost his will to live and requests to be taken off of life support or to be given a lethal drug to end his life. There are laws that allow a patient to be transferred to a hospice, where they will not be treated but will receive pain relief. Depending on the legal arrangements made, such as power of attorney, medical directives, and Do Not Resuscitate (DNR) orders, other people can be empowered to make these decisions on behalf of a patient. It is even legal in six states in the United States for a physician to help his patient commit suicide by prescribing a deadly drug for the patient.

Yet, does a doctor, family member, or even the patient himself have the right to end the patient's life? The values of society, which are constantly changing, may say "yes," but our holy Torah says, in no uncertain terms, "no!"

Laws are made to correspond to the values of a society. It is a fact that, as time goes on, ideas like "Death with Dignity" gain more support and are written into law. That's why, in situations like these, you may have to stand up and fight for what's right. When a doctor, next of kin, or the patient feel that they can and must make a decision to stop providing care or, G-d forbid, to actively end a patient's life, you are no longer in a situation of *bikur cholim*. In such a case, the Torah tells you, "Do not stand idly by your brother's blood."[3] It is now a situation of *pikuach nefesh*.

---

3   *Vayikra* 19:16.

This publication has been created to help you understand the ideas and values that motivate people in contemporary secular society, how these ideas differ from Torah values, and how to determine when you need to stand up and defend the sanctity of life as the Torah requires. What is written here is intended as a set of guidelines for thinking and is not to be viewed as the decisive halachic ruling, or *psak halachah*. Real halachic questions should be addressed to Orthodox Jewish rabbinic authorities who are qualified to answer them.

LIFE IS SACRED: A UNIQUELY JEWISH PERSPECTIVE

Contemporary values that support euthanasia and assisted suicide include the strengthening of personal autonomy, reducing the suffering of the ill, and protecting the sick from the loss of their dignity as a result of illness. These are indeed important goals to be achieved as part of the process of caring for and treating the ill. But there is something that is missing from this equation, something that may be the most important value in the Torah: the sanctity, or *kedushah*, of human life.

Life is sacred because all living beings were created by Hashem. Two verses express this fact in the Torah's account of Creation. One verse states, "And Hashem created the giant creatures and all of the living beings that creep, swarming in the waters according to their kind, and all types of winged birds according to their kind."[4] The second verse states, "And Hashem made the animals of the earth according to their kind, and the cattle according to its kind, and all creeping things according to their kind."[5]

While all life possesses the sanctity that comes from being created by Hashem, man is exalted above all other creatures in holiness, specifically because he was created in the image of Hashem. The Torah distinguishes man from all other creatures in this way; with regard to the rest of creation, the verses mentioned above state that Hashem made them "according to their kind," while regarding man, the Torah tells us, "and Hashem created the man in His image."[6] Animals, in the story of Creation, are mentioned in plural terms, while man is mentioned as a singular being. This important distinction tells us that while all living creatures are important to Hashem in a general way—like when we say, "the animal kingdom"—when it comes to human beings, each and every individual is important.

We understand from the Torah's reference to man in the singular that if a single human life is destroyed, it is considered as if an entire world has been destroyed. And the opposite is true too. If a single human life is saved, it is considered as if an entire world has been saved.[7] The idea that any single human being is a "miniature world" and therefore worthy of saving is absolute. It doesn't matter what the costs of medical treatment are or what a patient's prognosis is. It doesn't matter whether a person is

---

4   *Bereishis* 1:21.
5   Ibid., verse 25.
6   Ibid., verse 27.
7   *Talmud Yerushalmi, Sanhedrin* 4:9.

young or old, healthy or sick, or what their life circumstances are. The holiness and meaningfulness of a human life does not vanish under any circumstance.

Because of the sanctity present in all life, we have a responsibility to protect and preserve it. In exchange for our efforts, we are allowed to make use of and benefit from the world's resources, as long as we take care not to cause unjustifiable destruction. There is a mitzvah, *bal tashchis*, a prohibition against causing needless damage.

Peace is also one of the most important values in Judaism. Yet, as Shlomo HaMelech acknowledges, there are, unfortunately, "time(s) for war."[8] Conflict is a reality of the world we live in. Yet, in teaching us about *bal tashchis*, our Torah tells us not to cut down fruit trees even during wartime, because people will need the fruit for food. The sensitivity we are supposed to have toward the beneficial things in this world makes the question stronger: how can anyone—especially a doctor—even consider the idea that the best outcome for a living, breathing human being is for him to die? If we are not allowed to let one life-sustaining apple from a tree go to waste, why would anyone think to switch off a patient's respirator?

---

8 *Koheles* 3:8.

LIFE IS MEANINGFUL

A lot of people, when they think of the pain and suffering of another person, conclude that a life like that is not worth living. And most of the time, when people consider euthanasia or physician-assisted suicide as an option, they do so out of compassion and empathy for that person. But our Torah tells us that this type of thinking is wrong. Compassion and empathy like this are misguided. To think that life is only worth living under certain conditions is against everything we believe as Jews.

When a person wonders, "What's the point in living if living means suffering?" his question is based on the mistaken idea that suffering makes life meaningless. Every human being will have to face pain, guilt, and death in his life; these three things are inescapable. Yet they do not rob life of its meaning. As a matter of fact, these things are often the most significant events in our experience. When a person can find meaning in his suffering, his entire life becomes worthwhile. It would be better to strengthen a person's ability to withstand challenges than to tell him that his difficult life is meaningless.

WHY IS MURDER WRONG?

Another way to understand Judaism's emphasis on the importance of the life of any individual is to compare

Judaism's and society's respective positions on murder. What makes murder wrong in societies is completely different than what makes murder wrong according to the Torah. The reason why most countries have laws against murder is because of the idea that murder goes against the very idea of a civilized society. It breaks the "social contract" that the members of a society have to uphold in order to maintain a peaceful order.

Of course, it is this very reason that can justify the taking of a person's life when he is considered dangerous or burdensome to society. Here's where the problem starts. Both the serial killer and the patient in a vegetative state "cost" society a lot in terms of resources. The serial killer costs society innocent lives, not to mention the expense of his capture, trial, and imprisonment. We can understand why a society would put him to death. But a vegetative patient also consumes massive amounts of medical and financial resources, and doesn't give back much. Should society keep him alive?

What about the elderly or people who appear to have a short time left to live? Medical professionals may not feel as motivated to save or prolong the lives of these people, even if it means that their lack of involvement will result in their death. Often, doctors refrain from performing life-saving operations on people whom they feel are too elderly or sick to invest in. A doctor's authority, coupled with the patient's vulnerability, can create a situation where the patient is defenseless against a deadly type of neglect.

A few summers ago, the Rabbi of our shul went away for a short summer break. During that time, he asked me to cover for his position. Included in the responsibilities would be any crises, funerals, hospital visits, and other pastoral duties.

One morning, I received a frantic called from a woman who was a member of our shul, who was calling me from Florida. Her elderly father was in the ICU, and there was a discussion whether they should take him off the ventilator or not. The woman's brother, who was the ill person's son, was a doctor in the northeast United States. He wanted to "pull the plug," end the old man's life, and get back to his medical practice. The woman, on the other hand, wanted to make sure that she was doing the right thing in the eyes of G-d, halachah, and our tradition.

I immediately called a senior halachic authority. He in turn called Rabbi A.J. Twerski, the renowned psychiatrist, who suggested that we speak with Rabbi Moshe Kletenik of Seattle, who is a world-class expert on end-of-life issues in halachah. I called Rabbi Kletenik and he told me that he needed to speak to the intensivist in the Florida ICU in order to better understand the situation. The next call I received was from the intensivist, who introduced himself and told me that he had never met someone as knowledgeable in medicine who didn't carry the title "doctor" as the Rabbi he had just spoken to from Seattle. He said they would keep the ventilator operating and that they would continue for another twelve days in that facility.

At the end of the next day, I received a phone call from the woman. She told me that she and her family had just spent "one of the best days in her life." She related that her father had woken up, was breathing well, and the ventilator had been removed. Her father had sat up, and with his family around him, had spent the day recounting funny stories, savoring precious memories, and sharing much laughter. And while her brother the doctor was none too happy with me, the family agreed that keeping their father alive had been one of their most important accomplishments. The father lived another couple of weeks before he left the world in a quiet, peaceful, and calm manner.

The Torah's ban on murder is completely different from society's. We don't believe that an act of murder is wrong simply because it's bad for society to have people killing each other. It's wrong because every individual's life is important to Hashem. If we are ever in a situation where we have to choose between saving someone's life or preserving society's resources, we ignore the so-called greater good and save that person's life.

The importance of the individual is also a basic tenet in Western democracies. In a secular democracy, however, the good of society overrides the importance of the individual. Without Torah, we might wonder, "Isn't it selfish to keep people with no hope of recovery on life support, when others who could survive need the equipment?" That's basic economic thinking.

First of all, as long as a person is alive, we don't believe that there is no hope. Second, the Torah view is the exact opposite from the secular view. Our Torah is clear: the importance of the life of an individual overrides the good of society. We don't consider economics when it comes to saving or prolonging life.

Thus, the Torah says, "For blood brings guilt upon the land."[9] "Blood" does not come second to "the land." Human life is not less important than society.[10]

We believe that life is meant to be given and taken away by Hashem alone. This most basic tenet is what makes euthanasia and physician-assisted suicide forbidden by the Torah.

---

9   *Bamidbar* 35:33.
10   Rabbi Moshe Feinstein, *Darash Moshe*, *Bamidbar*, *Parashas Maasei*.

Section II

QUALITY OF LIFE, EUTHANASIA, AND PHYSICIAN-ASSISTED SUICIDE

In general, the goal of healthcare practitioners is to provide healing for patients. But there is a question that is debated in society as to what happens when an illness has made life unbearable for a patient, or it seems that the patient is at the end of their life. Another way to describe this is to speak of a person's quality of life.

QUALITY OF LIFE

Quality of life has many definitions. One is the extent to which a person can live a "regular life," connect to his environment and family, and achieve his goals, hopes, and dreams.[11] Another may

---

11   "Quality of Life: How Good is Life for You?" University of Toronto Quality of Life Research Unit, Retrieved 14 October 2009.

be a patient's ability to function normally without suffering or pain, including the pain of medical treatment.[12]

Still another involves the dignity of the patient. Even though there is no single definition of dignity, it might include things like independence, privacy, self-esteem, being able to maintain one's own life standards, autonomy, and self-control.[13] Certainly happiness and freedom from pain are part of what increase a person's quality of life. No one can deny that illness and disease can rob a person of all of these things.

Quality of life is something that applies not only to people facing end-of-life issues, but even to unborn or newborn children who have life-compromising or life-threatening conditions. Without a belief in the sanctity of life, for example, people may choose to abort an unborn child, ending the child's life and sparing him and his parents the challenge of dealing with a "life that is not a life."

The quality of life of a critically ill patient often drops below a level that is acceptable to the patient (assuming the patient is conscious), to the medical professionals, his family members, and health proxies. What happens next depends on whether the Torah is the guiding principle or not. This chapter describes what can happen when decisions are made with secular values, as opposed to Torah. It is important for you to be informed and

---

12   McNally, James W. (2009), *Encyclopedia of the Life Course and Human Development* (vol. 3 ed.), USA: Macmillan Reference, p. 317.

13   Telfer, E., "Philosophical Approaches to the Dilemma of Death with Dignity," from www.euthanasia.com.

aware of these ideas, because someday, you may have to step in and advocate for someone in this situation.

Supporters of euthanasia and physician-assisted suicide often believe that ending a person's life is justifiable once his or her quality of life has dropped below a certain level. At that point, many people will say that a person's life is "not a life." This idea contradicts the basic Jewish belief in the sanctity of life. Life is sacred, and there is nothing that can take away its sanctity, not even compromises to a person's quality of life.

When a patient's quality of life is greatly compromised, a decision is sometimes made to "let the patient go." This is a gentle way of saying, "let the patient die." Once this decision is made, there are two main ways to end a patient's life. One is through euthanasia, and the other is through physician-assisted suicide.

EUTHANASIA

Euthanasia is a Greek word that means, "good death." It is defined as "the painless killing of a patient suffering from an incurable and painful disease or in an irreversible coma."[14] It is sometimes called "mercy killing," because the person performing it on someone does this out of compassion for their suffering. Euthanasia can be active or passive.

---

14   From https://en.oxforddictionaries.com/definition/euthanasia.

Active euthanasia means that a person causes a patient's death through direct action, such as a doctor administering a lethal drug to the patient.

Passive euthanasia means that a person either withholds or withdraws treatment, and thereby allows the patient to die. Not performing surgery or giving medication that would allow the patient to live longer is one example of withholding treatment. Taking the patient off of life support, or "pulling the plug," is another. The patient then is left to die from his disease without the protection of life support. Transferring a patient from the hospital to a hospice facility is like passive euthanasia, because the patient is being moved from a situation where he is given treatment to one where he is not.

My friend's mother was quite ill and elderly and was in a major Toronto hospital. She seemed to be "winding down" in a calm and natural manner, without much pain and certainly no complaining that I heard. However, the family decided to withdraw all feeding tubes, which meant that she would get no liquid sustenance and no water. Essentially, she would be starved and dehydrated.

The family's doctor and the rest of the family overrode my friend's opinion and my vocal disagreement. They chose to remove all feeding and hydration tubes from her frail body. They assumed that her death would come quickly. But that was not what happened. Their mother lived for another three days, literally starving and dehydrating to death. Those days were filled with indescribable pain and suffering for her, yet the family and the medical staff in the hospital refused to do anything to better her condition.

A similar event occurred recently in the fall of 2017, where a woman continued to live for almost two full weeks with only small amounts of hydration but being denied food entirely. Her children, who were observant Jews, felt they were doing what was best for their mother and were fulfilling her wishes. The family members told me that it was horrible to witness and that the last days of her 98th year were terrible. While her mind worked well, her body was subjected to the slow painful death by starvation. This put a bitter end to a long and successful life.

Whether it is active or passive euthanasia, the patient dies as a result of commission (action) or omission (lack of action) on the part of the person performing euthanasia on the patient. He is responsible for the patient's death. The terrible irony that comes with this so-called act of compassion is that euthanasia often involves an excruciating death for the patient. Methods used commonly in many hospitals involve the withdrawal of feeding tubes and the denial of liquids to the patient. In other words, the patient is literally starved and dehydrated to death, a horrible process that can take several days to actually kill the patient, and traumatize anyone who is witness to it.

Euthanasia can be involuntary or voluntary. Involuntary euthanasia means that the patient is killed against his will, either because he does not want to die or because no one has asked him what his preference is. Aktion T4 was a program of involuntary euthanasia in which the Nazis put to death over 100,000 people whom they considered to be "enemies of the race," such as people who were physically or mentally disabled, terminally ill, or who carried genetic diseases. The Euthanasia Society of America, which still exists, used to press for involuntary euthanasia of people they thought were undesirable in society, including alcoholics. After the Nazis' brutality was exposed, the ESA only supported voluntary euthanasia. With a history like this, it is not surprising that involuntary euthanasia is illegal throughout the world.

Voluntary euthanasia is where the patient has requested to die, and has given informed consent for active or passive euthanasia to be performed on himself. Examples of voluntary euthanasia include a patient willingly refusing life support, medications, foods, or fluids. Voluntary euthanasia, both active and passive, is legal in a growing number of countries including the United States, Canada, the United Kingdom, the Netherlands, and Belgium. Some countries, like the Netherlands and Belgium, even allow voluntary euthanasia in the case of children.

There is another type of euthanasia, called non-voluntary euthanasia. This means that a patient is put to death or allowed to die without giving informed consent, because he is unable to give informed consent. This includes cases of people who are in a coma or persistent vegetative state. Their condition makes informed consent impossible. In such a case, three considerations are made: what the patient would have wanted if he could give consent, what the patient's health proxy decides in place of the patient, and what the doctor considers to be the best course of action.

Included in the category of non-voluntary euthanasia is child and infant euthanasia, which is performed on infants or young children who either have crippling birth defects or severe illnesses, and who cannot give informed consent. In such a case, a decision is made by the parents and medical professionals together. There are many considerations in cases like these, such as the child's quality of life, availability and costs of treatment, and the possibility of survival. Child euthanasia is controversial, but is legal in Belgium without age limit, and has been practiced in the Netherlands, the United Kingdom, and the United States. There have been cases in England and the United States where euthanasia was performed on children even without the parent's consent, such as the cases of Charlie Gard and Sun Hudson.[15] [16]

PHYSICIAN-ASSISTED SUICIDE

Physician-assisted suicide is an arrangement where the doctor helps a patient end his own life by giving him the means to do so under his supervision. It is defined as a doctor "knowingly and intentionally providing a person with the

---

[15] See http://lawprofessors.typepad.com/healthlawprof_blog/2005/03/lifesupport_sto.html for the case of Sun Hudson.

[16] Rabbi Elazar Flekeles was a close student of Rabbi Yechezkel Landau, the *Nodeh B'Yehudah*, and the Rav of Guttein in Moravia. When asked about the permissibility of bringing about the death of a severely deformed infant, he responded, "G-d forbid that any man would send his hand to injure or indirectly cause the death of such a child; one who does this is a murderer, and by his actions goes against the laws of Hashem and His Torah" (*Teshuvah Mei'Ahavah* 1:53).

knowledge or means or both required to commit suicide."[17] If the patient requests it, the doctor may, for example, prescribe the drug that will kill the patient. Or, the doctor can counsel his patient on how to take his own life.

What makes physician-assisted suicide different from active euthanasia is that the patient is the one who takes the drug or follows the physician's advice, and by doing so, commits suicide. What makes it different from passive euthanasia is that nothing has been withheld or withdrawn from the patient. The means of dying have simply been placed within the reach of the patient. Physician-assisted suicide is legal (at the time of this writing) in Canada, the United Kingdom, the Netherlands, Switzerland, Luxembourg, and Belgium, as well as in six states in the United States.

WHAT THE TORAH SAYS

Of all of the Torah's commandments, one of the most well-known is "You shall not murder—*Lo sirtzach*."[18] When a decision is made to take a person off of life support or otherwise withhold treatment from them, the result is death. In the secular world, this is seen as an exercise of a patient's right to die. But according to the Torah, causing someone to die or to die sooner than they would have is considered to be an act of murder.

---

17   From Euthanasia and Assisted Suicide (update 2007) (PDF), Canadian Medical Association, 2007.

18   *Shemos* 20:12.

Although we obey this commandment simply because Hashem told us to, we know that one of the reasons why murder is considered so morally wrong is because man has been made in the Image of Hashem. The prohibition against murder is not only something that applies to Jews or Jewish doctors. When Hashem gave Noah the Seven Noahide Laws, He said about murder, "One who spills the blood of man will have his own blood spilled by man, for in the Image of Hashem did Hashem make man."[19]

In order to understand how the Torah defines murder, we have to consider an earlier verse: "I [Hashem] will demand an accounting for the blood of your lives from every beast, from the hand of every man, and from the hand of every man's brother; I will demand an account for the life of man."[20] Chazal understand these two verses to mean that the sin of murder can manifest itself in several ways:

"One who spills the blood of man will have his own blood spilled by man," refers to a person who commits murder in the simple sense, without anyone else's involvement.

"I (Hashem) will demand an accounting for the blood of your lives," refers to a person who commits suicide. The

---

19   *Bereishis* 9:6. The Seven Noahide Laws (*sheva mitzvos bnei Noach*) were given by Hashem through Noah to all humanity, and they are binding upon everyone, both Jew and non-Jew, although Jews were later given a much more intricate and complex law code. One of these seven laws is a commandment to set up courts of law to prosecute those who violate the laws. When the verse says, "one who spills the blood of man will have his own blood spilled by man," it means that a person who commits murder is liable to capital punishment, meted out either by a court of law or Hashem Himself.

20   *Bereishis* 9:5.

German word for suicide is *selbstmord*, "self-murder." Suicide is considered to be the taking of a life, even though it is directed at the self. Suicide is considered to be a form of murder under certain circumstances in Jewish law, and even when a suicide does not meet the criteria for murder, it is an act that goes completely against the basic tenets of Judaism.

"From every beast" refers to a situation where a person has tied up another person in front of an animal so that he will be attacked by the animal. While the culprit is not the immediate cause of the victim's death, he has exposed his victim to a lethal risk from which the victim cannot escape. There are many situations similar to this in hospitals, where a patient dies by being exposed to deadly risks, such as being taken off of life support, which allows his illness to kill him.

It may not appear to an observer that the medical professional who has "pulled the plug" has killed the patient, because he or she did not use his or her bare hands or a weapon to end the patient's life. There is an indirect relationship and an amount of time that passes between the doctor's "pulling the plug" and the patient's death. Nevertheless, this is considered to be an act of murder by the Torah, and nobody, no matter what his or her qualifications are, has the right or authority to do this.

"From the hand of every man's brother; I will demand an account for the life of man," refers to a person who hires others to murder another person. Third parties require relatives' consent to end the life of a patient when the patient can't give it, as is the case with non-voluntary euthanasia. The family members, loved ones, or other relatives who legally empower medical professionals to remove life support from a patient, have essentially made that patient's death possible.

Although each successive case involves less direct action on the part of the person arranging for another's death, all four cases are considered instances of murder. The initiator, whether he takes the life of his fellow with his bare hands or arranges things so that another person's life ends, is either a murderer or an accomplice to a murder. That person will have to give an accounting before Hashem.[21]

Euthanasia, defined as "mercy killing," is considered to be murder under Jewish law. Whether the victim is healthy, terminally ill, or in the throes of dying, causing the death of another person, even under the mild-sounding term "medical aid in dying," is punishable by death by the Sanhedrin according to the Torah.[22]

The Torah does not ever allow us to judge a life as not a life. The burden of having a loved one in a vegetative state, for example, can be crushing to that person's family members. It may seem to an outsider that such a life bears no resemblance to life as we know it. Yet, we are obligated to prolong the life of that person and to give treatment should that person fall ill in the same way as we would be for a fully-conscious patient, even to the extent of violating Shabbos in cases of *pikuach nefesh*.

21　Maimonides, *Mishneh Torah*, Laws of Murderers and Guarding One's Life, 2:2.
22　Ibid., 2:7.

When Rabbi Avraham Grodzenski—one of the eminent Torah leaders in prewar Europe—was hospitalized during the Nazi occupation of the Kovno ghetto, his students came to impart grave news. They had gotten word that the Nazis were about to burn down the hospital, and they urged their beloved mentor to leave immediately. He thought for a moment and then said, "I am too ill to be transported, and without ongoing intensive medical care I will not survive. Evacuate whoever you can, and then move me to the top floor."

His students couldn't argue with their revered teacher, because they realized that he knew his condition better than they did. However, they tearfully asked, "What good will it do to move you further up?" Rabbi Grodzenski replied, "When they burn the building, the fire will reach the top floor last, so I will have a few more minutes of life."

OWNERSHIP OF ONE'S LIFE AND BODY

In the previous chapter, we learned about the idea of quality of life, euthanasia, and physician-assisted suicide. Remember that, according to our Torah, no one, not a doctor, health proxy, next of kin—not even the patient, is allowed to end the life of a patient or to facilitate the death of a patient. Ending someone else's life is murder. It's that simple.

You might be wondering what motivates people and societies to allow "mercy killing." What is the basic premise that permits people to overlook the importance of each and every person, and the sanctity of life? In this chapter, we will learn about the philosophy behind ideas such as quality of life, euthanasia, and physician-assisted suicide, and what our Torah's position is on these issues.

PERSONAL AUTONOMY AND THE "RIGHT TO DIE"

It is important to understand the factors that lead people to choose to let a patient "go." One of the most important values in a Western democracy is personal liberty. Liberty means that you are free to live and act as you choose, and that no one has the authority to make those decisions for you as long as you are a free member of society. Basically, you own your life.

The most basic thing a free person would have control over is their body. Many people believe that every individual is the owner of his body. As such, he is allowed to use it in any way he wishes. From body piercings to suicide, self-ownership is the foundation of a person's "right to choose" in contemporary society, even if it means choosing to die.

This concept, when we think of a patient in a healthcare setting, is known as patient autonomy. Patient autonomy preserves a person's right to decide how and if to accept or refuse medical treatment.

Patient autonomy can be a stronger or weaker value, depending on the culture. In some cultures, the doctor's relationship to the patient is more paternalistic. This means that the doctor has more power to decide on the patient's treatment plan than the patient or family members. The doctor can decide which medicines the patient has to take for his condition. He can determine which surgeries the patient should undergo. He can even decide, based on his diagnosis, that there is no hope for the patient and that no treatment should be given. In other cultures, this relationship is less paternalistic and the doctor and patient work more in partnership.

Patient autonomy is, in general, a very positive thing. Since we are commanded by the Torah to be responsible for our health, it is better to live in an environment where an informed individual has the final say in his own medical matters. Patient autonomy makes possible our ability to ask for kosher varieties of medication, or to state our preferences as to the gender of the doctor we choose to consult. It also enables us to put our doctors in touch with our rabbis and have them work together so that our healthcare and our service of Hashem can be the best possible.

Patient autonomy has a downside, too. Our Torah empowers us to be responsible for the upkeep of our health, but there is a point where a line is drawn. When it comes to issues of life and death, there is no patient autonomy, only a requirement that everything be done to prolong or save the life of a person. Because the life of each and every one of us is so precious to Hashem, He does not give us a "right to die."

OUR LIVES BELONG TO HASHEM

The idea that we own our bodies—and that ownership allows us to do anything we want with our bodies—sounds nice, but it contradicts what the Torah tells us. It is forbidden, for example, to cut your own flesh or make permanent markings on your skin.[23] A lot of people in the ancient world used to do this to mourn their dead. Today, many people have tattoos because it is fashionable. A Jew is not allowed to cut himself or have ink permanently inserted under his skin.

There is another explanation given regarding the prohibition against self-harm and self-mutilation. It was the custom of certain non-Jews to scar their bodies as part of an idolatrous ritual. The marking branded a person as a servant of his idol.[24] The Torah does not allow Jews to imitate these practices even if the intention is not idolatrous or for the purpose of mourning.

If tattoos and body piercings, which are meant for cosmetic purposes, are forbidden, all the more is this true for actions that are harmful or fatal. The bottom line is, it is forbidden for someone to injure himself.[25]

A Jew is not even allowed to have his body donated for scientific research after death. This is the case, even though medical research performed on a corpse can yield results that can be helpful in increasing our understanding of human health and, ultimately, helping others. Rabbi Moshe Feinstein, *zt"l*, was once asked by Rabbi Moshe Sherer, *z"l*, president of Agudath Israel of America, whether or not it was permissible to have one's body donated for scientific research. Rav Moshe's response was, "No one has ownership over his body to the extent that he can command that others use his

---

23   *Vayikra* 19:28.
24   *Sefer HaChinuch*, *mitzvah* 253.
25   See *Bava Kama* 91a; Maimonides, *Mishneh Torah*, Laws of Injury and Damage, 5:1.

body, even one organ, for any purpose. This holds true even for medical research."[26]

Under ordinary circumstances, meaning that the Jewish People are not oppressed or subject to any form of religious persecution, it is even forbidden for a Jew to choose death over the violation of a Torah commandment. To do this would make him liable for loss of his own life.[27]

If an individual does not have ownership of his body, no one else does either. Even where the patient cannot give informed consent, the Torah does not empower his relatives to direct medical professionals to take actions that can cause harm to or hasten the death of that patient.[28]

It needs to be made clear to every Jew that Hashem is the One Who owns our bodies, and therefore, we are not allowed to cause ourselves harm or choose death. Furthermore, no one is allowed to do this on someone else's behalf, whether it is a child, relative, loved one, or a medical professional. In Hashem's eyes, there is no difference between a doctor, family member, or the patient on this point.

Each one of us has been created by Hashem and sent to live in this world at a specific time for reasons known to Him alone. We all exist for a purpose, and each of us has a special

---

26   *Igros Moshe, Yoreh Deah* 3:140.
27   Rambam, *Mishneh Torah*, Foundations of the Torah, 5:1; The only exceptions to this rule are the three cardinal sins of murder, forbidden relationships, and idolatry. In these three cases, a Jew must choose death if the only two options are to commit these acts or be killed. See *Shulchan Aruch, Yoreh Deah* 157:1.
28   Ibid.

mission to fulfill on Earth. Since we do not know the nature of Hashem's Divine plan, we are not in a position to decide when we enter or leave this world.

Section IV

PAIN AND SUFFERING

Is it ever justifiable to allow a patient in agony to die? We mentioned before that one of the premises for the notion of the right to die is the importance of reducing the suffering of the ill. Avraham Reches, an Israeli professor of neurology, once said, "There is no principle or belief that can coerce a person to continue to suffer without hope."[29] But Professor Reches was mistaken. There is an explicit set of principles and beliefs set forth in the Torah regarding the right decision to be made under such circumstances, and these principles are G-d-given. Pain and suffering, as much as we would never wish these things on anybody, do not justify suicide, euthanasia, or physician-assisted suicide.

This is illustrated by a story in the Talmud. Rabbi Chanina ben Tradyon was a great teacher and spiritual leader at the time when the Romans dominated Eretz Yisrael. The Romans forbade the study or teaching of Torah because its values were contradictory to Roman ideals and laws, and gave the Jews hope to one day be free of their oppressors. Rabbi Chanina ben Tradyon was caught teaching Torah in public.

---

29   From http://www.haaretz.com/opinion/.premium-1.635434.

The Romans apprehended him, wrapped his body in the parchment of a Torah Scroll, surrounded him with bundles of dried grapevines, and lit him on fire. They also placed sponges of wool that had been soaked in water on his chest near his heart to prolong his pain and suffering. Clearly, the Roman enforcers did not want Rabbi Chanina ben Tradyon to die quickly.

The daughter of Rabbi Chanina ben Tradyon asked him, "Father, how can I bear to see you this way?" He answered, "If they only burned me, it would be difficult for me. But since I am being burned with a Torah Scroll, I know that the One Who will demand an accounting for the desecration of a Torah Scroll will demand an accounting for my desecration." The students of Rabbi Chanina ben Tradyon advised him, "Open your mouth, so that the flames will enter you!" He said to them, "It is better that He Who gave me my soul should take it, rather than I should injure myself."

There are many lessons to be learned from this Talmudic passage. One is that when the Jewish people are oppressed and prevented from learning or teaching Torah, they are obligated to give their lives for it. This is true even though human life is the most important value in the Torah.

Rabbi Chanina drew a parallel between the Torah scroll and himself, which teaches us that human life is as valuable as the Torah itself. The sanctity of human life is one of the most basic beliefs we have as Jews. But what could be holier than the holy Torah? Every night, we recite the words "*ki hem chayeinu v'orech yameinu*—the Torah is our life and length of our days." At the same time, if a person's life is in danger, we are obligated to violate almost every Torah law in order to save him. We are even required to violate Shabbos because of *pikuach nefesh* if it means prolonging life even for a moment.[30]

Rabbi Chanina refused to follow his students' advice to act in order to hasten his own death, even though his agony must have been indescribable. Our natural compassion for people can lead us to identify and empathize with a person whose suffering is so bad, he wants to die. Nevertheless, even in such a situation, the Torah's value regarding the sacredness of human life is the guiding principle, as Rabbi Chanina demonstrated.

The Torah is the source of our values and morals. The medical ethics committee is not. This being the case, the Torah, which is the expression of Hashem's will, is what determines right and wrong in cases of life and death.

REDUCING SUFFERING

One of the most persuasive arguments for physician-assisted suicide is that a person should be able to choose death when his or her life is completely unbearable because of the pain of his or her illness. The thinking goes, "He shouldn't have to live this way." But euthanasia activists play upon the fears that people have about pain, suffering, and death. They make it seem as if a patient's only choices are agony or euthanasia. This is nothing but pure, politically-motivated manipulation on their parts, and

---

30   *Shevus Yaakov* 1:13; see also *Yoma* 85a.

we have to make sure that we don't fall for it. The fact is, there is so much that can now be done to relieve the pain of illnesses.

PALLIATIVE CARE

Palliative care is a multidisciplinary specialization that seeks to improve quality of life through the control or elimination of pain, suffering, and distress in a variety of different health-related situations. Palliative care developed out of the hospice movement. Both approaches have the goal of providing patients with relief from pain. But while hospice care is intended for patients whom doctors regard as untreatable, palliative care is applied wherever pain management is needed.

Even in cases of people who do not need extensive treatment, palliative care is given. For example, the prescription of antidepressant drugs for the relief of depression is an example of palliative care. Even taking an aspirin for a headache can be considered palliative in the sense that the aspirin's effects cloak the symptoms of the headache.

Palliative care is especially helpful for people afflicted with life-threatening or life-limiting illnesses or conditions, and is administered widely in such cases. Advances in palliative care in the last few decades have led practitioners to conclude that "pain can be controlled in most patients."[31]

---

31   Miller K.E., Miller M.M., and Jolley M.R., (2001) *Challenges in Pain Management at the End of Life*, American Family Physician, the Journal of the American Academy of Family Physicians.

More than twenty years ago, an article was published by the American College of Physicians regarding the ability to control or eliminate pain associated with cancer. The authors stated,

> Today…most cancer pain can be controlled or even eliminated. For example, even with advanced cancer, pain can be controlled in 90% to 99% of cases. In nine out of ten cases, physicians can control pain by using pills alone; they do not have to use injections, operations, or other methods. In those few situations in which pain from cancer cannot be eliminated completely, it can be reduced so that the person with advanced cancer can live with it day to day and still accomplish activities that are important to him or her.[32]

Advances in palliative care have important ramifications in Jewish law. It is forbidden to withhold treatment or life support from a patient. Just as a patient is not allowed to give up one second of his life, no one else is allowed to do anything that will bring his death sooner, either. It has long been the case that palliative treatments can control or eliminate most forms of pain.

There are certain cases in Jewish law where taking active measures that will temporarily extend the life of a patient but will cause him pain and suffering are also forbidden. When pain can be controlled or eliminated, however, it is completely forbidden to disrupt any treatment aimed at extending the life of the patient. This becomes more the case with the passage

---

32   From: American College of Physicians, Cancer Pain, American College of Physicians, 1997, reference: http://www.acponline.org/public/h_care/3-pain.htm.

of time, as advances are continuously made in palliative care. These advances make pain and suffering less of a factor in illness and medical intervention, and make more rare the instances where we must withhold life-extending treatment.[33]

WHEN LIFE AND TORAH COMPETE

Life comes before nearly everything in Judaism.

A verse in the Torah states, "And you shall guard My statutes and My laws which if a person does them will live through them; I am G-d."[34] The Torah and its commandments are the central pillar of our lives as Jews, as we pray, "They [the words of Torah] are our life and the length of our days." Jews throughout history have willingly given up their lives to remain Torah-observant.

In the Gemara, quoting the verse, "And you shall guard My statutes and My laws which if a person does them will live through them," Chazal make the following inference: "'Live through them'—and not die through them." Our Sages understand this verse to mean that *pikuach nefesh* takes precedence over almost all commandments, including Shabbos.[35]

For example, if a person has an illness that is considered medically dangerous, no matter where it is on his body, we are required to break Shabbos in order to treat him. This

33   Rabbi Moshe Feinstein, *Igros Moshe*, *Yoreh Deah* 2:174:3.

34   *Vayikra* 18:5.

35   *Yoma* 85a-b.

is the case even if doctors disagree about the necessity of breaking Shabbos for a particular patient.[36] If a patient with a dangerous illness refuses to take medicine that has been prescribed for him, we are obligated to force him to take the medicine.[37] Even here, the patient does not have the choice whether or not to try to save his own life. On the other hand, if a patient claims that he needs a certain medication and the treating physician opines that he does not, we defer to the patient, unless the doctor states that the medicine will be damaging to the patient. In that case, we defer to the doctor.[38]

For the sake of healing, we are even obligated to give a dangerously ill patient foods that are *treif*, even mixtures of meat and milk, and even *kelei hakerem*.[39] This is true even if the patient has enjoyment from them. In the case of a person with an illness that is not life-threatening, we can only give them these remedies if they will not impart any pleasurable benefit. But we can still use non-kosher foods for healing purposes. Life comes first.

---

36   *Shulchan Aruch, Orach Chaim* 328:10.

37   *Magen Avraham*, ibid.

38   Ibid.

39   *Shulchan Aruch, Yoreh Deah*, 155:3.

GOSES: WHAT IS THE PROCEDURE IF SOMEONE IS CLEARLY DYING?

Choosing to die is not an option, whether a person is clinically depressed but physically healthy, or suffering from a terminal illness. People do not own their bodies or their lives. It is completely forbidden for a person to relinquish even a second of his or her own life, even if that person has very little time left in this world. What about people who seem to be at the end of their lives, who are, G-d forbid, in the throes of death? Are we allowed to assist the process of the soul leaving the body?

At this point, it is important to state what was stated in the introduction to this booklet. The points made here are to give the reader a framework for thinking. Any and all halachic questions that arise from actual situations must be discussed with a qualified rabbinic authority.

There are several rabbinic opinions as to how to approach a person who is referred to in halachah as a *goses*, meaning that, from what we can observe, he or she is definitely in the process of dying. Some authorities require us to force the patient to accept all forms of medical care, even at this point. Others permit the withholding of certain types of medications that cause pain to a person whose life is pure agony, when the patient is of sound mind and is able to request this. Even according to the second opinion, which allows a patient to refuse medications that cause pain, life-sustaining nutrients and respiratory support must continue to be provided to the patient in order to save his life.[40]

Because a *goses* is considered to be a living person in all aspects, we do not behave as if the person has died already, whether that means closing his eyes, preparing his body for burial, or removing our shoes and rending our garments. As long as a person is alive, we may continue to hope and pray for his or her recovery, because Hashem's ability to heal or save a person is unimpeded.

An important idea arises out of this, namely, that we do not regard any person's situation as hopeless. Even where a patient's condition is critical, we don't communicate messages of despair to him. This is true, despite a doctor's prognosis that his illness is untreatable or his condition is irreversible. It is an act of cruelty to rob a patient of his desire for recovery. We must never give up hope for a person's recovery, as long as he is alive.

For example, one of the things we do to prepare a deceased person for burial is close his eyelids. Jewish law does not allow

---

40   The overriding principle in this situation is that "one second of repentance in this world is greater than life in the World to Come." Suffering is a catalyst for repentance and, ultimately, atonement. See Rabbi Shlomo Zalman Auerbach, Responsa *Minchas Shlomo*, 1:91:24.

us to close the eyes of a dying person or to relate to him in any way that we would after his death. This is akin to pronouncing him dead already. To do this contradicts the most basic faith in Hashem, Who can heal a person no matter what his or her situation might be.

Yet, we still recognize that someone who is considered a *goses* is in a very delicate state. For this reason, no one is allowed to touch him. Any physical contact can quicken the patient's death. Someone who physically interacts with a *goses* before the actual departure of that person's soul is considered to be a murderer under Jewish law.[41]

> There was once a man who was in the process of dying and was unable to speak. A family member consulted with a very prominent rabbi[42] to ask if he should continue to be given nutrients through the feeding tube. The rabbi told him no; this would be a problem of physically interacting with a *goses* and could hasten the patient's death. Months later, a man came into the rabbi's office and told him, "I was that *goses*. And I can't tell you the suffering I had to go through when I heard that they would not feed me. If I had been able to speak at that time, I would have asked them to." Upon hearing this, the rabbi changed his ruling for the future.

This story embodies the words of Chazal, who said, "Even if a sharp sword rests on a person's throat, he should never

---

41   *Shulchan Aruch, Yoreh Deah* 339:1.

42   This rabbi was considered to be one of the greatest halachic authorities of his generation. His name has been withheld out of respect for his dignity.

stop hoping for mercy."[43] There is no point at which we give up on Hashem's ability to save a person's life. That is why no one is allowed to facilitate another person's death, even when it is someone who appears to us to be near death. As long as a person lives, there is hope.

Section VI

WHAT YOU CAN DO

A devoted family member, rabbi, *bikur cholim* volunteer, or a close friend can be a savior for anyone in a hospital or healthcare setting. By interacting with patients, comforting them, finding out what their needs are, and communicating them to the staff, you not only perform an awesome kindness, or *chesed*, for a Jewish person in need; you also make everyone else's job easier. By being in contact with doctors and nurses, you can help patients and their families understand what is happening, and who the right people are to ask to get their needs met. Sometimes it's your smile or just your availability that is the most important thing for the patient.

You may come across situations like the ones described in this booklet, where a patient or family member is being asked to make an "end-of-life" decision. There might not be anyone there besides you who knows what the right choice is at that time. How can you be of help then?

PATIENTS' RIGHTS

All free societies have laws protecting the rights of patients to be treated in accordance with their wishes. All Jewish people involved with the ill should know what a patient's rights are. You may have to defend them in the event that the medical professionals, other family members, or the patient himself is ignorant of them.

Patients' rights charters may differ in wording from country to country, but they are basically the same. The Association of American Physicians and Surgeons created the "Patient's Bill of Rights" in 1995, as follows:

All patients should be guaranteed the following freedoms:

- To seek consultation with the physician(s) of their choice

- To contract with their physician(s) on mutually agreeable terms

- To be treated confidentially, with access to their records limited to those involved in their care or designated by the patient

- To use their own resources to purchase the care of their choice

- To refuse medical treatment even if it is recommended by their physician(s)

- To be informed about their medical condition, the risks and benefits of treatment, and appropriate alternatives

- To refuse third-party interference in their medical care, and to be confident that their actions in seeking or declining medical care will not result in third-party-imposed penalties for patients or physicians

- To receive full disclosure of their insurance plan in plain language, including:

    1. CONTRACTS: A copy of the contract between the physician and healthcare plan, and between the patient or employer and the plan

    2. INCENTIVES: Whether participating physicians are offered financial incentives to reduce treatment or ration care

    3. COST: The full cost of the plan, including copayments, coinsurance, and deductibles

    4. COVERAGE: Benefits covered and excluded, including availability and location of twenty-four-hour emergency care

    5. QUALIFICATIONS: A roster and qualifications of participating physicians

    6. APPROVAL PROCEDURES: Authorization

procedures for services, whether doctors need approval of a committee or any other individual, and who decides what is medically necessary

7. REFERRALS: Procedures for consulting a specialist, and who must authorize the referral

8. APPEALS: Grievance procedures for claim or treatment denials

9. GAG RULE: Whether physicians are subject to a gag rule, preventing criticism of the plan

Of course, some of these freedoms will conflict with the Torah, such as the patient's right to refuse treatment in certain instances. But in general, these are the guidelines that exist outside of halachah to protect patients. They hold medical professionals accountable to working with patients "on mutually agreeable terms."

One item that is missing from this list is a requirement that a physician discuss all treatment options with a patient. If a patient is informed of all of his options, he will be able to access them. However, discussing all treatment options is a problem for anyone involved in containing costs in the healthcare industry. As physician-assisted suicide becomes viewed as a treatment option by society, patients might find that their insurance companies will pay for lethal drugs administered by doctors, but not other treatment options. This has already happened in the State of Oregon, where expensive life-saving drugs might not be covered under the Oregon Health Plan, but cheaper, lethal drug prescriptions are.[44] That means that people who are less able to afford the healthcare of their choice might be more likely to be prescribed assisted suicide.

ADVANCED PLANNING

It is always better to be prepared for certain circumstances than to have to make decisions in a crisis. One of the ways Jewish people can be prepared for these situations is by making sure that they have a halachic medical directive already in place. A medical directive is a legal document that outlines the patient's wishes for his treatment and care in case he ever, G-d forbid, becomes too ill or incapacitated to communicate them to medical professionals.

Medical directives are also called living wills, advance directives, advance healthcare directives, or advance decisions. These documents specify what actions are to be taken on behalf of a patient in this condition. People who are not Torah observant often use a medical directive to request to have life supports withdrawn or withheld. Observant Jews, however, can take advantage of this legal instrument to ensure that, should they lack the ability to state their preferences, they will be treated in accordance with halachah.

Agudath Israel of America and the Rabbinical Council of America have released halachic medical directives that accord

---

44   See http://abcnews.go.com/Health/story?id=5517492&page=1 for the case of Barbara Wagner.

with legal requirements by state. These have been modified for use in Canadian law, which places more emphasis on the importance of a health proxy, meaning that a patient's own wishes may be less binding than the testimony of a health proxy. This legal mechanism does not yet exist in England. Although the Chief Rabbinate is involved in certain cases, such as declaration of brain-stem death, a halachic medical directive does not exist in Israeli law. Regular Israeli medical directives have to be renewed every five years.

HEALTH PROXY

Another way to secure treatment in accordance with halachah is for a person to legally appoint a substitute who would be able to express his wishes, should he become unable to do so due to illness. There are many different types of documents that are used to name a healthcare proxy, but all of them empower the person named to make medical decisions on behalf of the patient.

Advance directives are important because they legally bind the treating physicians to facilitate the care of patients and any post-mortem actions in accordance with strict Orthodox Jewish law. Without incontrovertible proof of the patient's advance care wishes, there is less protecting the patient from a doctor making decisions on his behalf that may contradict Torah. The case of *Scardoni v. Hawryluck*, which took place in Ontario, Canada, is an example:

In *Scardoni v. Hawryluck*, Mrs. Joyce Holland was not in a vegetative state or brain-dead. Mrs. Joyce Holland was medically stable with recurrent pneumonia and only cognitively impaired on account of her Alzheimer's disease. In short, Mrs. Joyce Holland was very much alive when the physician proposed to withhold medically beneficial treatments for her pneumonia, namely the use of a ventilator and isotropic drugs which would require an admission to the intensive care unit. During the relevant times, Mrs. Joyce Holland was able to breathe spontaneously but not sufficiently, and therefore she was not totally dependent on the ventilator.[45]

Joyce Holland was not Jewish, but Catholic. According to her daughters, she had always told them, "Where there is life, there is hope," which they understood to mean that they should do everything possible to sustain her life as long as she was alive. The doctor's proposal was based on the idea that life support might keep Holland alive but not cure her disease. Alzheimer's being a degenerative disease, Holland was only expected to get worse, and would likely experience discomfort from life support and medications. At the beginning, the court actually decided in favor of the doctor because the daughters' status as health proxies did not meet a certain legal requirement. After the daughters appealed the court decision, the judge put the doctor's proposal aside and ruled in favor of Holland's daughters' refusal to comply with his plan.

---

45   252004 Carswell Ont 424: 5 E.T.R. (3d) 226, 12 Admin. L.R. (4th) 67, 69 O.R. (3d) 700, para. 33.

It is frightening to think that a doctor would have been legally empowered to euthanize his patient based on his own idea of quality of life. Yet, this is becoming more and more of a reality, particularly where plans have not been made in advance. It is important to ask a patient or his family members if they have a halachic medical directive or an arrangement for a health proxy in place. If they do not, you can help the patient and his family by directing them to organizations such as Chayim Aruchim. They will then have access to information, halachic medical directives, and the contact information for Orthodox rabbis who can assist them with any medical decision.

IN MOMENTS OF CRISIS

Very few people ever sign a medical directive, even though they are legally effective throughout the United States and Canada. That means that, in many cases, the patient, or more likely, the patient's family members, are faced with having to decide what to do when the patient has reached the "end-of-life" stage. This stage may last only moments, but it can also last for hours, or weeks. The patient's loved ones may never have imagined being in such a position, or may be in a state of shock and unsure of what to do. They may find themselves subjected to pressure to approve a "Do Not Resuscitate" (DNR) or similar order which means that their family member will not be given CPR or other rescue measures should their systems fail. At times, this pressure may come from the doctor, who feels that the patient's condition is "medically futile," or the insurance company, the hospital administration, or the medical ethics committee.

It is important for you to know that in both the medical and rabbinic fields, there are several definitions of death, including cardiopulmonary (heart-lung) and brain death, and that even within these definitions there are differences of opinions as to when you can declare it. That means that there can be a disparity between the medical staff's opinion and the halachah. Sometimes this disparity can have terrible consequences.

For example, every hospital has transplant surgeons on staff whose job it is to harvest still-functioning organs for patients waiting for life-saving transplant operations. Since the likelihood of organs being usable is much higher the sooner after death they are removed, transplant surgeons often advocate for the earliest possible moment that a patient can be declared medically dead. Without an advance directive, there may be nothing to protect the patient except for his family members, who may be in a state of shock, as well as uneducated about how to make a right decision in this scenario.

Dr. G. is a doctor in a Toronto hospital who, among his duties as a medical professional, is the head of the Medical Ethics Committee of the hospital. There is a protocol that he established wherein a patient must meet nine criteria before he is considered to have died and his organs can be harvested. One day, he saw the "organ harvest team" walking down a corridor of one of the wards, heading toward a particular room. He asked what the story was and whether all nine boxes had been checked off as having met all of the necessary criteria that he and his committee had determined. He was told the patient had met eight of the nine criteria, and the harvest team was certain that he was dead and they were intent on harvesting the organs as soon as possible. Dr. G. pushed back and insisted that they wait until all nine criteria were met. The conversation got quite heated, but Dr. G. held his position firmly and refused to bend the criteria. It was nine or nothing. The patient never met the ninth criterion. So the harvest team was turned away angry, disappointed, and empty-handed. The next morning, Dr. G. went to check on the status of the patient. And he found him sitting up in his bed, eating a bowl of breakfast cereal.

HOW TO HAVE THE CONVERSATION

If, G-d forbid, you or someone you know is ever in the position of having to decide what to do under pressure, there are some important points to remember. The Torah does not allow any human being to advise another to end someone's life, much less to take any action that will cause another person's death. There is no difference between a layperson and a doctor on this point. All people, no matter what their condition, no matter how long they have to live, are equal in the Torah's protection of their lives.

With this in mind, if you or anyone else is under pressure to make "ultimate" decisions concerning a patient's life, you are now in a situation of *pikuach nefesh*. You have been commissioned to save the life of a fellow Jew. Not being a medical professional, it is normal to feel intimidated. Please realize that doctors are simply human beings. They are fallible, they make mistakes, and their opinions are not the absolute truth. You don't need to be afraid of them. If you are the one person who can represent Hashem and His Torah now, you have all the authority you need to direct the professionals around you to do what is right.

You will need talking points for that conversation. With a tone that combines respect and firmness, articulate the following:

- The patient is Jewish, and as his representatives, we want to state clearly that all decisions concerning his life and health must be made in accordance with Orthodox Jewish law.

- We submit to qualified Orthodox Jewish legal authorities for all matters like this.

- In order for you to receive a decision concerning the patient, please speak to Rabbi (name), who can be reached at (number). We defer to him for any and all decisions concerning the life and health of this patient.

There are several important objectives that this conversation can accomplish. First, it takes the discussion out of the philosophical framework of contemporary society and clarifies that only Jewish law is to be the guiding principle for this patient. Second, the burden of responsibility for any decision is removed from the doctor and shifted to the rabbinic authority who will render that decision according to halachah. Third, it deflects any attempt to convince family members or health proxies to agree to euthanasia or physician-assisted suicide. Fourth, it stalls any action on behalf of the medical professionals, whose own opinions may favor euthanasia.

GOOD AND BAD ADVICE

The Torah tells us, "You shall not place a stumbling block before a blind person—*Lifnei iver lo sitein michshol.*"[46] Blind in this case does not mean a person who literally lacks eyesight. It means someone who does not perceive or understand something, an unsuspecting person.[47] Patients or family members who are uninformed as to their rights or choices are certainly in this category of people. In Jewish law, it is prohibited to take advantage of a person's ignorance and gullibility and give them bad advice.[48]

Of course, non-Jews and non-Jewish institutions do not operate according to Jewish law, and the principle of *"lifnei iver"* is either not a value in the same way, or has a legal equivalent that does not meet our needs. The morals and principles that exist in the societies around us are different

---

46   *Vayikra* 19:14.

47   *Sifra*; cf.; *Rashi*, loc. cit.

48   *Sefer HaChinuch, mitzvah* 232.

than ours. We must be prepared to defend our rights to the free expression of our religion in a non-Jewish society.

As a person who may be in a unique position to help, you can inform people that it is not only forbidden for a physician (or anyone else) to assist in a patient's suicide or to euthanize a patient actively or passively, it is completely against Torah law to even advise a doctor, patient, or a patient's family members or caregivers to participate in such things. Guidance and proper advice is an essential ingredient in a civilized world; advice that results in the death of a human being contradicts this principle altogether.[49]

You can help in all of these situations by engaging the family members, listening and supporting them in a moment of crisis. In a gentle but straightforward way, you can clarify the issues for them and help them to make a Torah-true decision about what to do for their loved one. In the long run, this is the most important gift you can give them, because you are helping the patient and his family live their values and to do what matters most. It will be much easier for these people to live with themselves, knowing that they did what was right for the person they loved.

Everyone involved in this type of situation needs encouragement. They need to be empowered. Let them know how valued their loved one's life is to Hashem. Help them to see that no one is allowed to allow a patient to die, and especially not to cause his death. Explain to them that a

---

49   *Sefer HaChinuch*, ibid.

doctor, with all of his authority, degrees, and experience, is no different from anyone else on this point. Remind them in a compassionate and supportive way that our Torah is clear about the obligation to prolong or save the life of the ill or dying, and that we must be prepared to demand this of anyone involved in the patient's care. Share what you know. You will free people from the bewilderment and confusion that comes from being in the position they are in, and give them the strength to advocate for life.

WHEN IT'S UP TO YOU

Most hospital patients are short-stay patients who eventually leave the hospital. However, the percentages of people who die in hospitals are quite high for the elderly or those who are there for extended periods of time.[50] A study revealed that, even without the possibility of euthanasia and physician-assisted suicide, a third of the people who die in hospitals die because of mistakes committed by the medical staff. This finding made hospital errors the third leading cause of death in the United States, a country with a very advanced system of medical care.[51] Think about how the growing trend of support for euthanasia and physician-

---

50   Margaret Jean Hall, Ph.D.; Shaleah Levant, M.P.H.; and Carol J. DeFrances, Ph.D., *Trends in Inpatient Hospital Deaths: National Hospital Discharge Survey 2000–2010*, NCHS Data Brief No. 118, March 2013.

51   http://www.hospitalsafetygrade.org/newsroom/display/hospitalerrors-thirdleading-causeofdeathinus-improvementstooslow.

assisted suicide can make a hospital that much more of a dangerous place for a patient.

> A resident in emergency medicine once told a family from our community to prepare for the end for their grandfather. A few days afterwards, he was home for Shabbos and was hosting guests.
>
> The doctor later said he was "mistaken."

You may not be able to prevent doctors' errors, but if you know that someone's life is threatened by the very people responsible for their well-being, and the patient or his relatives lack the ability to protect him, you may be the one who has to act. This can be very intimidating. If you have been a *bikur cholim* volunteer for any length of time, try to remember that you have already been a hero to many people. If you are the patient's family member, know that you have the power to save his life. Recall the words of Mordechai to Esther, "Who knows if for a moment like this, you have attained royalty."[52] Be strong and trust in Hashem, Who has made you His messenger.

---

52   *Esther* 4:14.

IN SUMMARY

This list is a summary of points made thoroughly and extensively in the booklet. The purpose of this list is to provide the reader with a basic review of its contents. This should prove helpful as an introduction to the subject as well as a set of guidelines in shorthand, in case the reader is already in the position of needing to advocate on behalf of a Jewish patient.

1. When a medical team decides that a patient's condition is "medically futile," there will be a values gap between the Torah's values and the values of contemporary society.

2. Our Torah does not empower anyone to end the life of a patient, whether that person is a doctor, family member, or the patient himself.

3. Every Jew is obligated to prevent this from happening, as the Torah says, "Do not stand idly by your brother's blood."

4. Life is sacred because all living beings were created by Hashem, and human beings were created in His Image. Each and every individual human being is important to Hashem.

5. There is no other factor that changes this basic premise, whether the cost of medical treatment or the condition of the patient.

6. The meaningfulness of human life does not vanish under any circumstance, including instances of suffering. Suffering does not render life meaningless and worthy of being ended.

7. People who support or advocate for euthanasia do so out of misguided compassion and empathy. The Torah does not support these ideas.

8. As Jews, we are obligated to protect and preserve human life.

9. Euthanasia and physician-assisted suicide constitute forms of murder, and they contradict the Torah's basic principle of the sanctity of life.

10. The life of each individual overrides any and all notions of the greater good, such as preserving the resources of a society. Human life is more important than society.

11. Since Hashem is the One Who gives life and takes it away, we know that there is always hope for a person's recovery.

12. Quality of life is not a Jewish concept. There is no such criterion in the Torah that justifies the ending of a human life.

13. Pain, suffering, and loss of dignity and independence are indeed problems that ill people face, and it is incumbent upon us to alleviate these as much as possible. Yet none of these conditions can ever take away the sanctity of life, nor do they allow anyone to decide that a life is "not worth living."

14. Whether euthanasia is passive or active, whoever facilitates the process is responsible for the death of the patient. Hastening an earlier death for a patient is a form of murder.

15. Euthanasia and physician-assisted suicide are often given softer-sounding names to make them appear like acts of kindness, such as "mercy killing," or "assisted dying." No matter what terms are or will ever be used to describe these actions, our Torah considers them either as murder or as an accessory to murder.

16. Euthanasia and physician-assisted suicide are never justified, even if the patient is elderly or in a vegetative state. The cost to society of maintaining any patient is not a consideration in judging a person's worthiness to live.

17. *Pikuach nefesh*, the obligation to save the life of one who is in danger, even supersedes our obligation to keep Shabbos, and it includes people who seem to have no hope for life.

18. The concept of a "right to die" is based on Western democratic ideas of liberty and personal autonomy,

i.e., that a person owns his body and can choose what to do with it, even to end his own life.

19. The Torah has no such concept of self-ownership to the extent that a person can choose death. Our lives are too precious to Hashem for Him to grant us a "right to die." He owns our bodies.

20. Patient autonomy can be a positive thing in the sense that we can make choices concerning our healthcare. The Torah's limit on autonomy is life-affirming, not a denial of the concept of liberty.

21. Patient autonomy also enables a patient or his health proxy to state, in no uncertain terms, that he wants to be resuscitated in any and all circumstances.

22. We do not have any right to cause harm to our bodies, whether injurious or fatal. If we are not at liberty to do these things, it stands to reason that nobody else is either.

23. Euthanasia advocates often take advantage of people's fears concerning pain, suffering, and death, and make it seem as if patients only have two options: horrible suffering or euthanasia. This is not the case. The field of palliative care is highly advanced, and in many cases, the pain of illness can be successfully alleviated.

24. When Jews are not in a state of religious persecution, there are only three very specific circumstances in which a person, under the guidance of a rabbinic

authority, might choose death over transgression. In any other case, we suspend all Torah laws in order to save another's life, and many of these simply in order to facilitate healing.

25. Even if it appears that a patient is in the process of dying, he must be provided with life-sustaining nutrients and respiration until his death. To remove these or to interact with such a person in any way that may hasten his death is murder.

26. All countries have laws protecting the rights of patients, enabling them to be treated in accordance with their wishes. We need to be educated and informed about these rights, so that we will able to fight for them if need be.

27. Advance legal planning for these circumstances through halachic medical directives provides protection for the patient from being treated in a way that contradicts Jewish law.

28. These advance medical directives are effective legal instruments recognized in many jurisdictions. By law, these obligate physicians to treat patients according to halachah.

29. Planning in advance also preemptively protects family members from the stress of having to make decisions under pressure from medical professionals, hospital administrators, insurance agents, or other family members.

30. Another way to plan for medical crises is to name a trusted family member or other reliable individual as a health proxy, who will be able to communicate the care requirements of his appointer should the appointer become unable to do so.

31. It is important to identify a qualified Orthodox rabbinic authority who is capable of making critical healthcare or end-of-life decisions, and to place him in charge of directing medical professionals in accordance with halachah.

32. In the event that you or someone you know is in the position of having to make an "ultimate decision" on behalf of a family member or other patient, remember that no one, not even the doctor, is authorized to terminate the life of that patient.

33. Doctors are valuable members of society who have special training, but they are only human beings and they make mistakes. As an advocate for the patient, you need to be able to communicate the patient's needs as well as ensure that Jewish law is respected.

34. If you have to converse with the staff, make clear to anyone involved in the patient's care that the patient is Jewish, and that all medical and healthcare matters concerning this patient are to be decided in accordance with Orthodox Jewish law.

35. Provide the name and contact information of the

rabbinic authority to whom you entrust these matters and state that you will submit to his decision.

36. Trust in Hashem that He will help you carry out this most important mission.

GLOSSARY

bal tashchis: the prohibition against causing needless damage.

bikur cholim: the mitzvah of visiting the sick.

bris milah: circumcision.

chesed: act of kindness.

gedolei Yisrael: great Torah sages and leaders of the generation.

gemilas chassadim: performance of acts of kindness.

goses: one who is in the process of dying.

halachah: the entire body of Jewish law; a specific law.

pikuach nefesh: saving a human life.

Shlomo HaMelech: King Solomon.

z"l: pronounced "zal," a Hebrew acronym for "*zichrono l'vrachah*"; "May his memory be for a blessing."

zt"l: pronounced "zatzal," a Hebrew acronym for "*zecher tzaddik l'vrachah*"; "May the memory of the righteous be for a blessing."